A Girl's Guide to Friends

Sharon Witt

Girl Wise® – A girl's guide to friends

20 19 18 17 16 15 14 7 6 5 4 3 2 1

First published 2013 by Collective Wisdom Publications.
This edition published 2014 by Authentic Media Ltd
52, Presley Way, Crownhill, Milton Keynes, MK8 0ES.

www.authenticmedia.co.uk

British Library Cataloguing in Publication Data
A catalogue record for this book is available from the British Library

ISBN-13: 978-1-86024-915-0

Design and cartoons: Ivan Smith, Communiqué Graphics, Lilydale, Australia.
Printed in Great Britain by Bell and Bain, Glasgow.

You are a wonderful, creative, inspiring,
cherished girl.

Inside...

Welcome

1 FRIENDS MATTER!
2 The importance of friends

5 MAKING NEW FRIENDS
6 Friendships don't just happen
10 How to make new friends
24 Qualities of a good friend
30 What does a great friend look like?
32 Friendship recipe
38 Why friends are like plants

45 BUILDING STRONG & HEALTHY FRIENDSHIPS
46 How can you make your friendships STRONG and HEALTHY?
49 The art of letter writing
52 Rights of a friend

55 FRIENDSHIP PROBLEMS
56 When friendships are NO fun
58 Peer pressure
62 Dealing with DIFFERENT personalities

75 A clash of personalities

77 Gossip

84 It's okay to be YOU!

86 Dealing with shyness

90 Opposites can attract

94 Be a FRIEND to yourself

97 FUN THINGS TO DO WITH YOUR FRIENDS

100 Chocolate balls recipe

102 Friendship affirmation journals

103 Painting a friendship canvas

104 Making a friendship board

106 Helping a friend

109 CONFLICT RESOLUTION

110 Bullying

112 Examples of bullying

113 Tips for dealing with BULLYING

114 What you can do if you are being BULLIED

116 Dealing with CONFLICT with friends

118 TIPS for talking through problems with your friends

122 In conclusion

Hi gorgeous girl!

Welcome to **GIRL WISE** – a series of books that have been created especially for **YOU**.

Why? Because you are an **INCREDIBLE** and **AMAZING** girl and sometimes you just might need a little bit of encouragement along the way to be reminded just how beautiful and capable you are.

This book has been created especially for girls just like you.

Friendships are an important part of our lives and it would be much more difficult if we had to go through life without them. But sometimes, things may go wrong. Misunderstandings can occur and friendship groups may change. It can be difficult to know the best way to handle it.

So I hope and pray that this friendship guidebook gives you some helpful advice along the way. I hope you enjoy reading it. Just know that you are **NEVER** alone. ☺

Love **Sharon**

FRIENDS MATTER!

The importance of friends

Where would we be without our FRIENDS?

I know that the world would be a pretty lonely place if we all just existed and didn't have special relationships with friends.

Friendships are GOD-GIVEN GIFTS – there is no doubt about it.

Friends are there to help us celebrate when things go well. For example, they'll be there with you to cheer you on when you get first prize in an art competition. They'll share your joy when a new baby brother or sister arrives. True friends are happy for us when good things happen.

Friends are also important when things don't go so well, such as when you lose a pet or you get a nasty case of chickenpox. Great friends do all they can to cheer each other up, lend a listening ear and just BE there for us.

'Friends love through all kinds of weather, and families stick together in all kinds of trouble.'

Proverbs 17:17 (MSG)

'Friendship is born at that moment when one person says to another: "What! You too? Thought I was the only one."'

C.S. Lewis

Throughout my life,
I have had many
different friendships.
Some of them have
lasted a year, some of
them were for a season – such as just
through primary school – and some have lasted
for years and years!

The important thing to remember is that all friendships, no matter how long they last, are there for a SEASON and a REASON.

Some friendships might have been especially important when settling into a new school, while others might have started because you were in hospital together for a short time. Other friendships might have started when you were a little girl, walking into your preschool with a pink backpack over your shoulder and a tear in your eye as mum drove away. Others may have naturally developed because you lived in the same street or close by.

However you meet a new friend, appreciate it as a gift.

We never know how long a friendship may last, but if you are really blessed, some may just last you a LIFETIME.

A true friend

A true friend is one that is loyal,
They stand beside you no matter what.
A friend offers support when you need it
Whether you ask for it or not.

A true friend will spend time with you
Even if they have a lot to do.
Because they see the value in what you have
Between each other, that is true.

Friends don't make judgements
Or tell you what you've done wrong.
They will stand beside you and offer advice
And stand with you when you're not strong.

Each and every one of us should know what
It means to have a friend.
That someone who knows you so very well
And on whom you can depend.

A true friend is loyal
No matter when and where.
If you have this kind of friendship
You are blessed beyond compare.

MAKING NEW FRIENDS

Friendships don't just happen ...or do they?

Think of your three closest friends for just a minute.

Do you remember where you first met them and how you became friends?

One of my closest friendships came from someone I met at the school where I teach. Ever since we first met, we've just made each other laugh, and laugh. It has always felt as if the chats and laughs have come so easily. Above all, we really **RESPECT** each other. That means, even if we disagree about something the other says, we stay friends.

Other friends I have formed over the years have come from living in the same street. Where we live, we're all very close to our neighbours in a lovely court. Almost every day, we'll see a neighbour and say 'Hi'. Many times, we've gone beyond the odd 'Hello' to find out what's happening in people's lives. The more we talk, the more we form friendships.

I've made many other friends along the way simply by being **INTERESTED** in others, **SMILING** when I meet someone new and **ASKING QUESTIONS** to get to know them better.

It doesn't take much to say hello to someone you haven't met before, but I am so glad I have done this on many occasions. If I hadn't tried talking with people, I would have missed out on some pretty awesome friendships.

'In order to make a friend, you have to be one first.'

Elbert Hubbard

Make a list of five friends

and where you first met them...

Name

Name

Name

Name

Name

How to make new friends

From the time you can speak and spend time with other children, you begin making new friends. You may have made friends during your preschool years or even through a playgroup. Sometimes, you might form new friendships through people that your parents know, even family members such as cousins.

Some girls find making friends **EASY!** They seem to just be able to walk up to someone new, smile, begin a conversation and away they go – another new friend!

Others, however, (maybe you) find it really difficult to make new friends. You might be shy or fearful that the other person may not like you or want to be your friend. Those feelings are perfectly normal and nothing to worry about.

'True happiness consists not in the multitude of friends, but in the worth and choice.'

Ben Johnson

Have you ever heard this phrase:

'FEEL THE FEAR AND DO IT ANYWAY'

Everybody feels quite **NERVOUS** or even **SCARED** when doing something different. It may be when you first meet someone new, or that moment when the teacher asks you to stand and talk in front of the whole class. But this phrase is saying, 'Yes, I'm a little scared and nervous but I'm going to have a go anyway!'

Remember this as well:

MEETING SOMEONE FOR THE FIRST TIME MAKES THE OTHER PERSON FEEL NERVOUS TOO.

I remember when I was younger starting at a brand new school. It was scary. I just did **NOT** want to go **AT ALL!** But Mum and Dad had made the decision and I had to go.

WHAT WAS I GOING TO DO?

It came time to start the new school. The weekend before, my head was racing with lots of worrying thoughts. I wasn't going to know **ANYBODY** on my first day!

Would I make a bad impression? Would the other kids think I was silly? Was my face going to make everyone laugh? Would anybody even talk to me?

Most of all, was my hair a joke?

That last question was the big one on the Saturday afternoon before I started at the new school.

I made a decision. **HAIRCUT TIME!** Yep, just the weekend before, I decided I would need to take **DRASTIC** action and cut my hair.

A whole new style!

A new look for me!

Never tried the new look before, but it had to be done, I thought.

I walked into the hairdressers, asked for a 'new look' and got exactly what I requested.

Walking out after the appointment, I took one look in a window and gasped.

OH NO! I've got sideburns!

The fringe! It's so **SHORT!**

What was I **THINKING?**

I had few choices.

Wear a wig? **NO.**

Fly to Brazil? **NOPE.**

This was one of those times when I would just have to 'feel the fear' and face it anyway!

Sure it was TOUGH at first. But it wasn't the end of the world.

And as for the girls in my new class, it took a little while but I did actually get to know them.

The more I made an effort to be **INTERESTED IN THEM**, the more they became interested in me.

The best part of this story is what's happening with those friendships now, 20 years later. Two of those girls I met (even when I showed up with a weird fringe and freaky sideburns) are STILL my precious friends today.

And do you want to know something else?
They **NEVER** mentioned my shocking haircut!

Tips for making new friends

> 'You can make more friends in two months by becoming really interested in other people, than you can in two years by trying to get other people interested in you.'
>
> Dale Carnegie

Be interested

Try and begin a conversation with someone new by showing that you are interested in **THEM** first. If she is new to your school, you might begin by asking what school she came from, what she likes to do for fun or how many family members she has. Once you begin asking questions, you are sure to find something in common to talk about fairly quickly.

Use eye contact

This probably seems like something **SO SIMPLE** but it's something that many girls forget. Even before you first go up to someone and begin a conversation, use eye contact. Look her in the eyes and make sure you

nod and smile. There is nothing more off-putting than having a conversation with someone who spends half the time looking somewhere else, as if looking for someone or something far more interesting!

Smile

A simple smile says **SO MUCH!** It says that you are willing to make a new friend. It says that you are happy to talk with the other person. It says that you are interested in getting to know her and that she is **VALUED.** Most importantly, a smile costs you **ABSOLUTELY NOTHING.** Come to think of it, you have a never-ending supply of smiles available, so make sure you use them **LOTS!**

Be yourself

The best advice – is to **BE YOURSELF!** No one else can be you and you bring something to your friendship groups that no one else does.

Sometimes, there is very real pressure on us to try and act like someone else. We can think that our personality

is boring and uninteresting. But that's not being real. The problem with not being yourself when you first make a new friend, is that you have to keep up appearances. That means, if you pretend that you **REALLY LIKE** rock climbing, pretty soon, your friend will want to go rock climbing with you because it's something **YOU** enjoy. Or maybe you say you love listening to a certain band. Before you know it, your new friend has just created a playlist and shared it with you. And you were just trying to sound impressive!

Just stop! The **REAL YOU** is fine and wonderful, and worth getting to know – even if your real hobby is collecting rocks!

Ask questions

When you are first getting to know a new friend (or haven't seen them in a while), make sure you ask lots of **QUESTIONS** to find out about the other person. Sure it's great to share your own stories and interests, but make sure you also ask questions to get to know the other person. (Have a look at the next page for some ideas.)

Friendship icebreakers...

Questions you can ask a new friend.

How many people are in your family?

What is the strangest/funniest pet you've owned?

What is your favourite television show?

What do you want to do whe you grow up?

Is there a pet you wish you could own but your parents won't let you?

Do you believe in God?

Which has been your favourite birthday and what made it so special?

Do you go to church?

Have you ever been to the circus and where was it?

What special talents do you have?

Which are you more scared of – mice or spiders?

What was your most embarrassing moment?

Who do you admire most and why?

If you could have an entire day to do anything you wanted, what would you do?

If you had a super power, what would it be and why?

Have you ever travelled overseas?

How many schools have you attended?

What would you change about yourself and why?

Do you play a musical instrument?

What is your favourite colour?

Who is your favourite band/ music artist?

What is the weirdest gift you've ever received?

What is your all-time favourite movie?

Do you have a favourite sporting team that you follow?

What is your favourite thing to do on a rainy day?

Do you have any strange habits?

Tips from real girls for making new friends...

'Be nice – not too crazy. And just remember to be yourself. Don't be friends with someone just because they seem to be popular. If they are not nice, or are a bad influence on you or others, you won't want to hang out with them anyway.'

Amy, aged 9

'I think it's important to be yourself and try to find a friend that likes you for who you really are.'

Rachel, aged 11

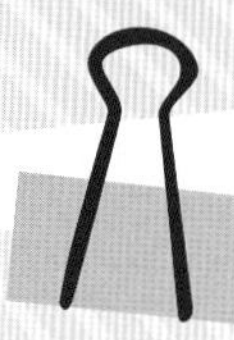

'My best advice with making friends is to make conversation first, be yourself and smile. ☺'

Tania, aged 9

'Be interested in their life. Ask them about their own interests.'

Paige, aged 10

'Firstly, you should smile politely. Then say "hello" and try to begin talking about a common topic, perhaps about school or about them.'

Joyce, aged 12

'Just SMILE and say HELLO!'

Collette, aged 9

'Be polite. Say "Hi" and make an effort to get to know someone.'

Romina, aged 10

'Be friendly and try to begin a conversation. Be yourself and try to make friends with people who seem like they might have similar interests to you. And a few really good friends is better than lots of people around you that you don't really like.'

Jamie-Lee, aged 10

Friendship quotes

'Be yourself, everyone else is already taken.'

Oscar Wilde

'A friend is a gift you give yourself.'

Robert Louis Stevenson

'Friendship and support from friends is something which is a source of tremendous inspiration always and to everyone.'

Nelson Mandela

'Friendship is the hardest thing in the world to explain. It's not something you learn in school. But if you haven't learned the meaning of friendship, you really haven't learned anything.'

Muhammad Ali

'Friendship consists in forgetting what one gives, and remembering what one receives.'

Alexandre Dumas

'A warm smile is the universal language of kindness.'

William Arthur Ward

'I have learned that to have a good friend is the purest of all God's gifts, for it is love that has no exchange of payment.'

Frances Farmer

'The proper office of a friend is to side with you when you are wrong. Nearly anybody will side with you when you are in the right.'

Mark Twain

'It is one of the blessings of old friends that you can afford to be stupid with them.'

Ralph Waldo Emerson

'The antidote for fifty enemies is one friend.'

Aristotle

'Never refuse any advance of friendship, for if nine out of ten bring you nothing, one alone may repay you.'

Claudine Guérin de Tencin

Qualities of a good friend

SO WHAT MAKES A GOOD FRIEND?

> 'Make sure that nobody pays back wrong for wrong, but always strive to do what is good for each other and for everyone else.'
>
> 1 Thessalonians 5:15 (NIV)

Good friends are special and valuable. There are many qualities that make a friendship great. Most girls think that you need to have similar interests and things you like to talk about but that is not always the case. Here are some qualities that friends should have.

Friendly...

It kind of makes sense doesn't it! A good friend will actually have the quality of being FRIENDLY. A friend should behave in a friendly manner – that is usually what attracts you to want to be a friend in the first place. A good friend should also be kind to your family and other friends. It doesn't cost anything to behave well.

Kind...

A good friend should always treat you with kindness. This doesn't mean she will always be having a good day and be happy and smiling, but a good friend always treats you in a kind and respectful way. If you say hello, she says hello back. She does not deliberately hurt your feelings.

Trustworthy...

Friendships need to be based on trust. This is a very important part of true friendships. You need to feel that you could share a secret or a problem with your friend without worrying that everyone will know about it tomorrow morning at school! A true friend listens, respects and offers advice but doesn't go and gossip about you.

Respectful...

A good friend always treats you with respect. She may not always agree with your viewpoint or what you believe, but she will still be your friend, no matter what. It is impossible to find a friend who you will agree with **ALL** the time, but you can find a friend who will respect you, even when you make a mistake or disagree.

Loyal...

Loyalty is an essential quality of a solid friendship. Loyalty means your friend will stick by you in front of other people. For example, another group of people may be talking badly about you without you being there. In those times, a true friend will speak out in your defence and not agree with others just to look good in other people's eyes.

Humorous...

Humour is not **ESSENTIAL** to every friendship – but it sure does help a lot! Laughing together is one of the best things about friends. You may laugh at the same jokes, or find the same type of movies hilarious. And being able to laugh and smile just helps build a stronger friendship.

Communicates...

Imagine calling up your friend on the phone and not getting much of a response when you ask questions. Imagine her saying nothing more than 'yes' and 'no' to everything you ask. Firstly, it would make the whole conversation a pretty boring one, but it would also make it difficult to know how your friend is feeling.

Good communication is important for any relationship, especially for keeping friendships in healthy, working order.

Selfless...

A true friend is selfless. This is not to be confused with the word selfish – that is the opposite to selfless. A friend that is selfless will sometimes play a game or go somewhere with you, even if that is not her favourite thing to do. Being selfless means being able to put your friend's feelings ahead of yours. For example, your friend loves bowling and really wants to have her birthday party at the bowling alley. It's not your favourite thing to do, but you agree it will be fun because it is something your friend would enjoy. After all, it's **HER** birthday party.

Honest...

Honesty is such a valuable part of a friendship. Without it, you don't really have a strong friendship. Being honest in a friendship means sometimes you might have to tell your friend something she doesn't really want to hear.

For example, your friend might ask you, 'Do you think my hair would suit me if I dyed it bright orange?' She may really want to dye her hair orange, but you should be honest if you think it's not a good idea. Don't just say, 'Sure, you would look great as a Mandarin!' to save her feelings. True friends can be honest with each other and the friendship will still survive.

Thoughts on being a GOOD friend...

1. I think it's great to have a broad range of friends. Don't just stick with one friend all the time or a small group of friends. You can hang around with them some days but hang around other people too. **BE INCLUSIVE**.

2. If you see someone lonely, go and ask her if she would like to hang around with you even if you would not usually spend time with her.

3. If lots of people want to hang around with you at the same time, or on the same day, you could organise days for them, e.g. Kate Monday, Chelsea and Sarah Tuesday, Rachael Wednesday.

4. Assume the best of everyone. Don't think that if some people aren't friendly towards you, they don't want to hang around you. They might be shy or a bit too 'out there'.

Luella Morgan, aged 11

What I love about my best friend

I love that my friend is always there for me. Even though we live so far apart and we only communicate via snail mail, she **NEVER** lets go of our friendship.

I love that I can be myself around her and she won't judge me for doing so. I also love that we always have a great time together no matter what is going on in our lives.

Adele Williams

What does a great friend look like?

'True friends will be there with you to share the giggles in the good times and cry with you in the bad times.'

Anonymous

On the picture below, write all of the qualities you appreciate in your friends...

My best friend

My best friend's name is **SOPHIE**.

Sophie is very funny and she cares about me
just as much as I care about her.

She is a bit of a chatterbox but I think that is great.

We like to talk a lot in class
and sometimes we get told off!

Sophie and I get to have play dates, which are always
lots of fun. We get to play together a lot!

She comes to every birthday of mine
and I get to enjoy hers.

Sophie loves the band One Direction,
but I think I'm one of her fans!

We love being able to tell our secrets to each other
and it's so great being able to talk
to your **BFF** (Best Friends Forever).

If we ever fight, we are always best friends
again before too long.

And when I'm older, I know that Sophie
and I will **ALWAYS** be friends.

Shonara, aged 8

Friendship recipe

Ingredients:

 ½ cup of friendliness

 ½ cup of loyalty

 2 teaspoons of humour

 A handful of trust

 A sprinkling of kindness and appreciation

Mix all ingredients together well.

Stir in a cup of communication and sprinkle daily all over your friendship.

Enjoy ☺

Advice on being a good friend

What makes a good friend?

If you are always caring.

Always help your friend out.

If they have a problem,

try to comfort them and

help them work it out.

If they are angry,

try to calm them.

You want to give your friend compliments.

Never be shy to ask your friend questions.

A good sense of humour goes a long way.

Don't push yourself to be a perfect friend.

Just **BE YOU!**

Mikaela, aged 10

What do your friends like about you?

'I am friendly, creative, smart + funny.'

Stephanie, aged 10

'My friends say I am great at making jokes, cheering people up and being kind.'

Lia, aged 9

'I am a pretty crazy friend. I love to have fun and hate being bored. I am often coming up with fun new games we can play and activities to do when we are bored.'

Becca, aged 10

'I am kind, considerate of others, but also fairly shy. I have some friends that are a bit more outgoing than me, which is good because they can help bring me out of my shell sometimes.'

Samantha, aged 11

'I am an inclusive friend. I like to make people feel welcome in our friendship group and help them to feel wanted. I hate seeing people on their own and sad.'

Gemma, aged 9

'My friends would describe me as humorous, encouraging, and always happy. I am also a very supportive and loyal frien

Mia, aged 11

Why friends are important

Friends are important to me
because when
I am sad or angry
I have them to comfort me,
care for me and
support me.

If I didn't have friends,
I would most definitely
be lonely.
If I am going on a school excursion,
I have someone to talk to.
I have some amazing friends.
Just make sure you don't
change for anyone!

By Star, aged 10

Favourite birthday celebrations

Girls like you share their favourite birthday celebrations...

'The best party I had was my 10th birthday when all of my church friends were there. It was really memorable because it was the first time I had many of my friends over and they all had a sleepover.'

Chloe, aged 10

'My most memorable birthday was my 8th birthday, when all of my friends from Year 2 came over. It was lovely because I got 26 birthday wishes from my friends and lots of lovely gifts.'

Joyce, aged 10

'My best birthday was one where I was simply spending time with my family and friends.'

Andrea, aged 10

'My best birthday with friends was when we all went to see a movie together at the cinema. I was allowed to invite all of my closest friends.'

Hayley, aged 10

'My favourite birthday celebration was when we set up a tent up in the back garden with all of my friends. We had pillows, cushions, sweets and had loads of fun.'

Tiana, aged 9

'I once celebrated my birthday by having a disco party at home. It was so amazing because I had all 30 of my friends there.'

Georgia, aged 11

'My best birthday was when my aunty took me away for the weekend. I was the first of my family members to see my cousin's brand new home. I felt really special!'

Anna, aged 10

'My favourite birthday party was where my mum organised an "Amazing Race". We were in teams and had to complete all these challenges in groups. My mum did a great job setting it all up. It was the **BEST!**'

Jas, aged 11

'When I was turning 8 years old I had a fairy party with my friends. We had so much fun and I got to wear wings. ☺'

Stephanie, aged 10

Why friends are like plants

Have you ever been given a seed or a small tree and planted it in the garden? If you have, you will already know that you cannot simply bury it there in the soil, leave it and expect a big, strong tree to grow up by next week.

If you simply plant your seed or tree and leave it, chances are it will not do **ANYTHING**. In fact, without care, it will probably wither and die.

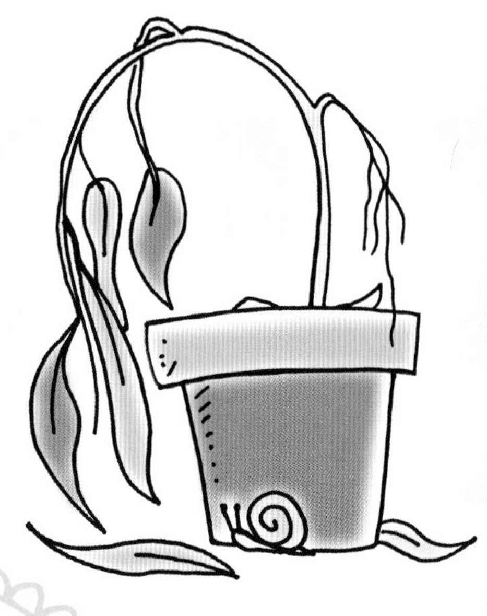

'But friendship is precious, not only in the shade, but in the sunshine of life; and thanks to a benevolent arrangement of things, the greater part of life is sunshine.'

Thomas Jefferson

'Friendship is like a flower. Once it has bloomed you still need to take care of it to stop it from withering.'

Aisha Dalal

Plants need to be watered regularly to keep the roots moist so they can grow. They also need to have regular food – or fertiliser – added to the soil and sunlight to help the tree grow big and strong.

A friendship is very much like this. It needs to be nurtured (taken care of) so that it can grow and become strong.

Thoughts on friendship...

Friendship is like a magnet that sticks us together.
Far away or together, we will always be with each other.
You can always make a connection something even better.
Never forget the times we were together.
Friendship is just better than ever.
You always have friendship with someone
even if it's your mother.
Nothing could keep you apart.
You will always be together for ever and ever.
Without a doubt, you will be back together for ever.
Nothing could ever compare to the friendship
that we have together.

Mieka Dalal, aged 12

Friendship demonstrates love.
It's about caring and helping other people who need your help. It could be help with school work or looking after their pets. Friendship shows how much people mean to you and how grateful you are to have them in your life. Friendship can be something as simple as going to the movies together or as important as going to a birthday together to celebrate.

Ashleigh Kirton, aged 11

REAL GIRLS

'Friends are some of the most important people in your life. They are people you can laugh and cry with, and be yourself in front of. To me, a true friend is someone who will always stick by you, no matter what: someone who accepts you for who you are!'

Persis, aged 13

'My friendship is sometimes up and sometimes down. I do talk to my closest friend a lot about hormones and things like that. In Year 5, I started to hang out and talk with my friends and not play games as much.'

Nadja Schneider, aged 10

'Friendship is a beautiful thing. It can make you laugh. It can make you cry, but friendship is all about the friends you have. It doesn't matter who you have known the longest. It's about having a ball with all your friends. It makes you want to do those things over and over again. It's about having those sleepovers that go far too quickly because you are just having too much fun. And when you go home, or your friends leave your house, you always remember what got you in stitches and laugh about it all over again.'

Isabella Campbell, aged 11

What friendship means to me

Hi my name is Alana.

I find it hard to make friends because I'm a bit different to others. I have learning difficulties and ADHD, which not all people understand.

Changing schools was quite hard for me because change can be scary and making friends can be hard.

But friendship and loyalty are very important to me.

Having friends that will stick by you no matter what – whether you are different or you are struggling or having a bad day – is important.

If they are still wanting to be your friend regardless, it shows that they are truly your friend and really do care.

And those who will encourage you to do what's right, will be patient and wait for you, include and accept you – they are **TRUE FRIENDS!**

Alana, aged 15

Friends

Friends are precious,
More precious than gold.
Friends are like treats,
They are very sweet.
Friends are always there for you,
Always by your side.
Friends are like flowers,
Bringing colour to your world.
Friends are always there for you,
Through the good times and the bad.
Friends will never let you down,
So no need to wear a frown.
Friends make you laugh
And can always cheer you up.
Friends will stand by you,
Stand by you till the end.
The love of a **TRUE** friend
Will never, ever end.

Tayla Williams, aged 11

'I think friendship means you know a person that cares for you and is always looking out for you. All my friends care about me as well as their other friends. If you and your friend have a fight, later you and your friend can make up. Everyone needs a friend because if you don't, you'll be very lonely. You and your friend can laugh together and cry together. With your friend, you can be silly without anyone judging you.'

By Olivia Millott-Jones, aged 8

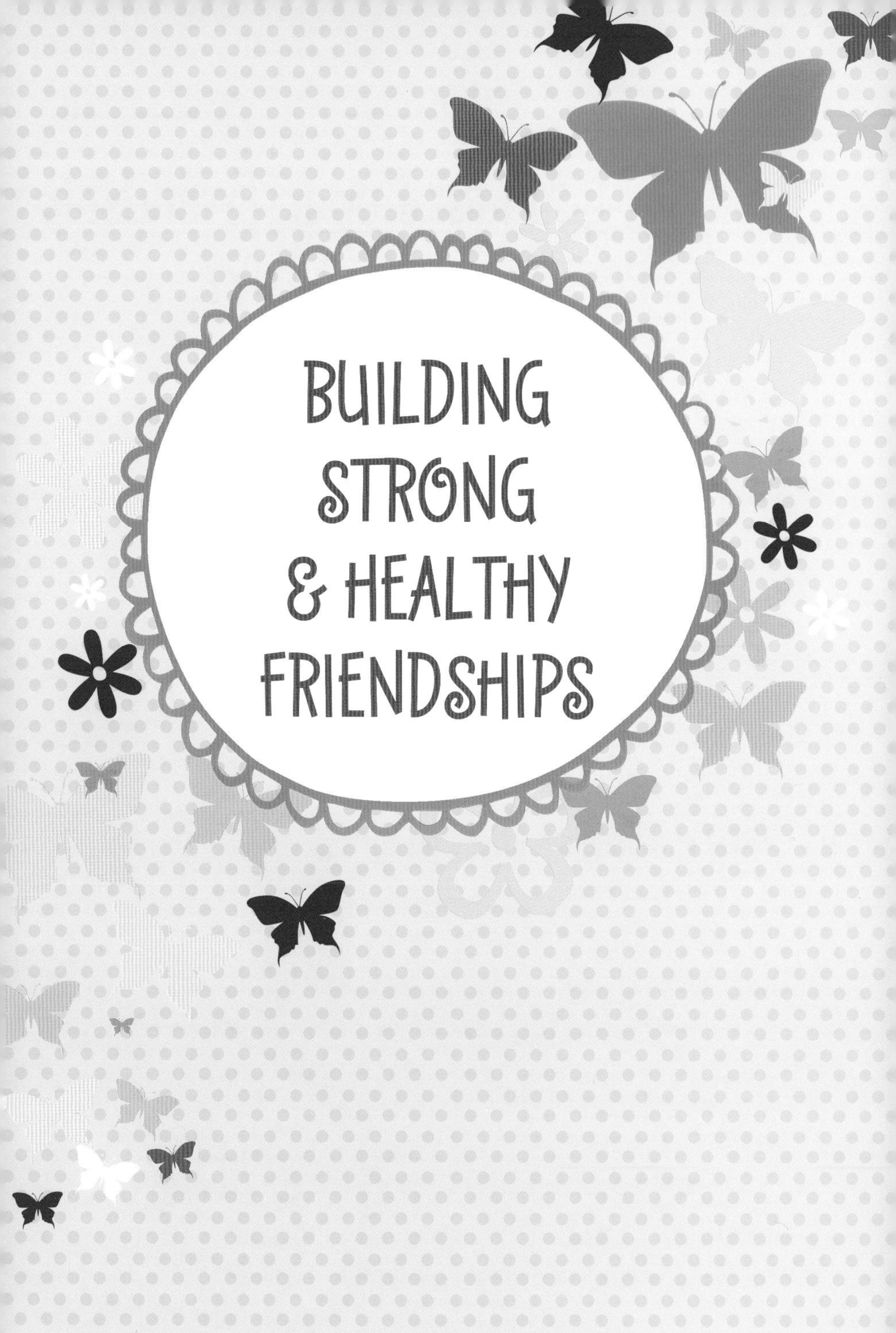

BUILDING STRONG & HEALTHY FRIENDSHIPS

How can you make your friendships STRONG and HEALTHY?

Spend time together

It sounds pretty simple, hey? Spend time together! Well that could be fairly easy. If you attend the same school as your friends, you could obviously see plenty of each other. But other friends might not live so close by, or perhaps you only see them at church or at netball practice. Sometimes you will need to make a SPECIAL EFFORT to connect with your friends. Why not invite your friend over to play or even for a sleepover?

Write encouraging notes and cards

If your friend doesn't live close by, don't let that stop the friendship from blossoming! Plenty of friendships have stood the test of time through letter writing and cards!

WRITE to your friend often and send encouraging cards. You can do a lot for your friend by communicating and offering encouragement.

'Since you get more joy out of giving joy to others, you should put a good deal of thought into the happiness that you are able to give.'

Eleanor Roosevelt

Communicate

Just like writing cards and notes, communicating with your friends is very important. Offering **POSITIVE WORDS** and encouragement to your friends through what you say makes a friendship stronger. When you talk about things openly, there's less chance of problems getting out of hand.

Laugh often

It is often said that laughter is the best medicine! Having **FUN** and **LAUGHING** with your friends is a healthy thing to do. It also has the added bonus of releasing your body's 'Feel Good' emotions when you laugh. It's great to have a good old belly laugh with your friends as often as you can.

Get creative

Doing something CREATIVE also helps to strengthen friendships. Spending time together – doing something that is fun and creative – is like putting a deposit into your friendship account. You could make a scrapbook album or even write a song together. Spending time together just creates some wonderful friendship memories.

Pray for each other

If you have a FAITH and believe in God, praying for your friends is one of the most wonderful things you can do. God hears our prayers and in praying for your friend, you are SHARING the problems they may be facing or giving them an extra measure of encouragement.

The art of letter writing

When I was a young girl, I would take the time to WRITE LETTERS to my Grandma most weeks. I would make sure I always had some pretty writing paper and envelopes on hand, and would sit down each week to write and tell her about my week.

The art of letter writing doesn't feel so important these days. Sure, you are taught to write properly when you are at school – how to write each letter of the alphabet and how to construct a sentence. But we are not often called on to write letters. Many people communicate these days through typing emails ('ELECTRONIC MAIL') and even instant messages on mobile phones and over websites.

But there is something wonderful about receiving a handwritten letter or card in the post. This would be especially great for a friend or relative living in a different part of the country, or even a friend you met on holiday once.

'There are high spots in all of our lives and most of them have come about through encouragement from someone else.'

George M. Adams

Keeping in contact through letter writing is a wonderful way to keep friendships – in fact, any type of relationship – going **STRONG**.

Don't know how to write a handwritten letter properly yet?

Here's an example on the next page. I've even shown you how to address the envelope correctly too! Why not write a letter to someone you know this week and give them a **LOVELY SURPRISE?**

Cassie Brown
14, Westacot Way,
Berkley, Victoria, 3152
18th October

Dear Jenny,

How are you doing? I hope you had a lovely week.

This week at school we have been studying mini-beasts. It was a lot of fun as we have been collecting little bugs from all over the playground.

Jesse even brought in a spider that he found in his shed at home. Mrs Jones has put it into a fish tank, with no water of course!

How is your horse? Thank you for sending the photo of him. The name Rusty really suits him! It must be lots of fun riding him around your farm.

Mum and Dad said we might be able to come and visit you next summer. That would be so great if we were able to come.

Well, I must go now. I have to go and clean out my rabbit's cage.

Much love

Cassie xxxx

Jenny Smith
12, Anywhere Street
Cambridge
CB3 1GH
United Kingdom

Rights of a friend

So, having friends is a great responsibility. As we've already discussed, being a friend to someone means you also have to put in some work. It shouldn't always be hard work (more on that later) but all friends should get some basic things right. These are qualities and behaviour you should expect and deserve from a friend.

TRUST

You should be able to trust a real friend. You should expect that she will keep things that you tell her private, especially if it is something very personal that you don't want the whole world knowing about.
If she does share your secrets with others, you need to let your friend know that it is not okay. (By the way, there may be times when you need to tell a friend's secret to an adult if you are worried about her health or if someone is hurting her. Talk to your parent or guardian about times like these so you know what to do if it ever happens.)

CARE

Your friend should always show that she cares about your welfare – how you are doing right now – and your feelings. If a friend is nasty to your face or behind your back, you have a right to let her know that she has hurt you.

RESPECT

A true friend should always show respect to you and your belongings. For example, a friend should not simply go through your pencil case at school just because you are her friend and probably wouldn't mind. A friend respects you enough to ask first! A friend should also respect you in the way she **TALKS TO YOU** and **ABOUT YOU** to others.

And **YOUR** friends should be able to expect the **SAME** from you in return. ☺

'Many people will walk in and out of your life, but only true friends will leave footprints in your heart.'

Eleanor Roosevelt

The true meaning of friendship

Some people will be your friend
because of whom you know
Some people will be your friend
because of your position
Some people will be your friend
because of the way you look
Some people will be your friend
because of your possessions
But the only **REAL FRIENDS**
are the people who will be your friends
because they like you for how you are inside

Susan Polis Schutz

FRIENDSHIP PROBLEMS

When friendships are NO fun

Friendships that are NOT too healthy for you

Unhealthy friendships can feel a bit like a vacuum cleaner sucking all the energy out of you. Unhealthy friendships are basically friendships that are one-sided. That means one person is always doing everything and having to help out the other one.

Sure, it's true that all great friendships will be tested at times but it is important to remember that it should work like a true partnership. In simple words, it needs to work for BOTH of you!

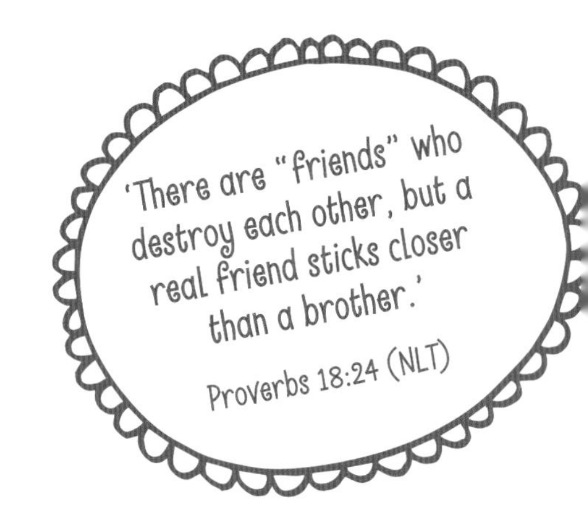

Needy friends can be quite difficult – the friend who has a low self-image will often complain that she is 'stupid' or 'too ugly' or 'nobody likes me'.

My advice for supporting a friend like **THIS** is to tell your friend that she is **IMPORTANT** and **WORTHWHILE**. Try not to encourage the excessive self-criticism that produces frequent phrases like 'I'm fat', or 'I'm ugly'. If you begin to get worried about her health, of course make sure you tell an adult. But otherwise, try to ignore negative behaviour, as it will only bring you down too, and you don't need that!

Peer pressure

Peer pressure is basically feeling pushed to do something that you don't feel **COMFORTABLE** about.

Imagine this scene from a preschool playground:

Two kids say to you, 'Throw sand at Becky.' Right there and then, that's peer pressure and you have a choice to make.

To throw or not to throw?

As you go through primary school, the choices you face might be a little more advanced, like 'Do I follow my friends and go out of bounds during breaktime?'

Decide now that you'll always choose the best decision for you, no matter what. That way, it won't be so difficult when you face the pressure to do something that you're not comfortable with.

'Escape quickly from the company of fools,
they're a waste of your time,
a waste of your words.'
Proverbs 14:7 (MSG)

How do I know what the right decision is?

We all have an in-built system that helps us when we are faced with a difficult decision to make. It is called your **CONSCIENCE**.

Your conscience is that feeling in your stomach that helps you know whether a situation is right or not. It also helps you to make the right decision, not the wrong one.

For example, a friend may say to you, 'Can you go to the teacher's desk drawer and grab a pen for me?' You know, deep down in your tummy, that you aren't supposed to go into that drawer without asking.

When you **THINK** about going up to the teacher's desk, opening the drawer and taking a pen, you actually feel uneasy and a bit sick in your stomach. **THAT** is your conscience, your inner voice, telling you that it probably isn't the right decision.

If you are not sure whether you are about to make the right decision or not, try this:

Imagine you have just made the decision to go up and take the pen from the teacher's desk. Really think about what that would be like. How do you feel? Are you **HAPPY** that you got the pen for your friend? Are you **NERVOUS** that you have gone to your teacher's desk drawer without permission? Do you **FEEL** that you have done the wrong thing?

Once you have thought about what this would feel like, you should have a fairly good idea of what decision you should make!

'Become wise by walking with the wise; hang out with fools and watch your life fall to pieces.'

Proverbs 13:20 (MSG)

DIPS – peer pressure points

When you are faced with the pressure to do something you are not sure about, try the following:

DELAY

Don't be pressured into doing something that doesn't feel right to you.

IMAGINE

Imagine you have already made the decision. If you have made the wrong decision, you will feel anxious, uneasy or worried.

PRAY

Praying about the best decision to make can help make you peaceful about your decision – giving you the assurance in your heart that it's okay.

STOP

Don't make a decision straight away. Give yourself **TIME** to think it through.

Dealing with DIFFERENT personalities

We have all been created **UNIQUE** and **WONDERFUL** girls. Having different personalities is actually a great thing. The world would be incredibly boring if we were all the same!

For example, can you just imagine if **EVERY** girl in the world was shy and didn't enjoy spending a lot of time with other people?

Or imagine if every girl was loud and excitable and always wanted to be the centre of attention? Can you just imagine everyone talking and laughing over each other all the time?

'A friend is always loyal, and a brother is born to help in time of need.'

Proverbs 17:17 (NLT)

You will no doubt have **DIFFERENT FRIENDS** throughout your life with **DIFFERING PERSONALITIES**. They might include:

Humorous

Quiet

Thoughtful

Strong

Excitable

Vivacious

A Leader

Friendly

Inquisitive

Shy

Smart

Energetic

Opinionated

Inclusive

Introverted

Look up any words you don't know the meaning of in your dictionary. ☺

Think about your
five closest friends.
Describe their personalities.

Name ______________

Three words to
describe their personality

____

____

____

Name ______________

Three words to
describe their personality

____

____

____

Name ______________

Three words to
describe their personality

____

____

____

Name ______________

Three words to
describe their personality

____

____

____

Name ______________

Three words to
describe their personality

____

____

____

REAL friendship problems

Questions from girls like you

'At my school, there is a large group of popular girls and my best friend is popular, but I'm not. How do I deal with this?'

This is such a common problem, sweetheart – more common than you would probably realise. We often place other girls in the 'popular' club, but what does it really mean to be popular? I guess it means that you are well liked, friendly with the 'cool' girls and invited to hang out and play with others. It sure can feel pretty lonely when you are not feeling well liked or 'popular' with other girls. In fact, it can really hurt to feel on the outside of things.

Try and remember that you are a strong, amazing girl and those who are 'popular' actually shouldn't determine how you feel about yourself. Your best friend hangs out with you because you are a **WONDERFUL** person. Perhaps those other girls just need a chance to spend time with you and get to know you better, and all your amazing strengths, qualities and personality!

Make sure you take time to do some special things with your friend – things that will lift your spirits. But don't let others make you feel inferior (less than you are). You are wonderful!

'When I was in spelling group the other day, I overheard some of the popular girls talking about how much they hate my best friend. What should I do? Should I tell my best friend what I overheard?'

What an unfortunate thing you had to hear! It's really, really difficult when we hear others speaking negatively about someone we love. It hurts us too, doesn't it!

I wouldn't go rushing to tell your friend about what you overheard. Sure, those girls were being most unkind about her, but telling your best friend may only cause her to feel bad about herself. Just make sure you focus on building up your best friend and being extra kind and supportive to her.

REAL GIRLS

'I have a really good friend, but sometimes she is just so full-on to hang around with. I feel like I can barely take a break from playing with her. Sometimes I would like to play with someone else, but she is always by my side. What should I do?'

Sometimes, for one reason or another, a friend can be quite overbearing and seem to need a lot of extra time from us. That can be quite exhausting. It could be that she hasn't got a large circle of friends, or perhaps she's having a tough time at home. Nevertheless, we **ALL** need our own space. As much as you like spending time with your friend, she also needs to allow you space and time to spend with others.

You need to be careful here about your friend's feelings. If you feel that you are able to, you could try the following conversation starter:

'Hey Jen, you know I appreciate you heaps and love being your friend, but I am going to play with Lucy and Sarah at lunchtime today because they asked me to. You are welcome to join us, or perhaps you would like a turn at playing with someone new too? I can meet you back at the classroom door at the end of lunch if you like?'

If you don't feel comfortable having a conversation like this, perhaps you could help your friend make some other friends as well. The more friends, the merrier! Perhaps start off by doing a group activity at breaktime, such as hopscotch or tag. Once your friend has the opportunity to broaden her friendships, she may not be so clingy.

'My friend often says mean things to me, although says she's only joking. But after a while, it becomes very annoying. What should I do? It's starting to really get me down?'

Many girls use humour as part of communicating with others. But saying mean things to others (even if you **ARE** joking) is not helpful at all. You will probably need to talk to your friend about how this upsets you. Be kind, and speak gently with your friend. Choose a time when you can both be alone together and let her know that you are having a problem that you need to talk with her about.

Gently explain that when she makes comments like that, somewhere deep inside, your heart keeps telling you it's no joke. Explain how you feel and that you understand that she may not even realise how it can come across. Tell her how much you appreciate her as a friend but that you would feel so much better if she didn't joke with your feelings in that way. Remind her how it affects you, if she continues.

If you still don't get very far with your friend, you may need some assistance from an adult to talk with your friend, such as your teacher or a parent.

'I really LOVE to read! I would actually read during every break at school if I had the chance. The problem is, some girls are starting to say I never make time for them, complaining that I am always reading. But I enjoy reading so much. What can I do?'

Reading is such a relaxing and fun thing to do! I know, because I also **LOVE** to read. But sometimes, we need to make space for other things. And just like we need to look after plants in our gardens, we also need to take care of our friendships and spend time **NURTURING** – or looking after – them.

This means that as much as we would love to, reading during every break at school might mean that your friends don't get to hang out with you as much, doing fun things.

My advice here is to perhaps set aside two breaks each week when you will read. Then, during the other breaks, go and play with your friends. Make sure you tell your friends that you **LOVE** to read, and will set aside two breaks during the week at school to read. Tell them the days and times. Once they know that they are also important to you, they should understand that you need your reading space too. Then you are **FREE** to enjoy playing time with your friends, and they will have the privilege of spending time with you!

'A girl at school yesterday handed out her birthday invitations in front of me – except I wasn't invited! It was so embarrassing and I couldn't believe she would do that in front of me. I am SO upset, I cried last night at home!'

Sometimes in life, awful and embarrassing things can happen to us. It can be falling down the stairs at school in front of everyone, or spilling your drink down your T-shirt. We all have yucky things happen to us occasionally.

It is very sad that a girl at school felt she couldn't invite you to her party, even though it seems like she invited almost everyone else.

Often, it is very difficult to understand why someone would behave that way – especially when **YOU KNOW** that you wouldn't treat others that way.

All you can do in a situation like this is to hold your head high, even though on the inside – and quite possibly on the outside – you are crying with pain and feelings of rejection.

Try and find out when the party is, and plan to do something extra special with your mum, sister or grandma the same day. It's okay to tell Mum or Dad what happened and why you want to do something special. I'm sure they will understand! Replace that yucky feeling with some happy memories. ☺

'I have a big problem. I have two friends but they both really dislike each other. Basically they don't get along and they BOTH want to play with me. Help! What should I do?'

Wow! It sounds like you have two very different friends with differing personalities. It is common for some friends to not get along but this makes it **VERY** difficult for you, having to try and keep the peace.

If they cannot agree to get along and are going to fight or disagree in front of you, this will not be helpful. So, the best thing to do here is to spend time with each friend separately.

'I'm really, really shy, and want to make new friends. Any suggestions?'

Many girls are shy and this can make it just that little bit more difficult to make new friends.

My first piece of advice is to **BE YOU!** You are worth getting to know and worth spending time with.

The best quote I have ever read is one by a man named Elbert Hubbard. He said: **'IN ORDER TO HAVE FRIENDS, YOU MUST FIRST BE ONE!'**

So, even though you are quite shy, **YOU** can be a friend to someone else first. And I'm quite sure there are other girls out there as well that are also shy and in the same boat as you.

Try looking out for other girls who look like they are by themselves and not hanging out with others. Go up and introduce yourself and say 'Hello'. Yes, this is quite scary at first, but it does get better with practice!

Put a smile on your face, and **RELAX**. Before you know it, you will have made a new friend. ☺

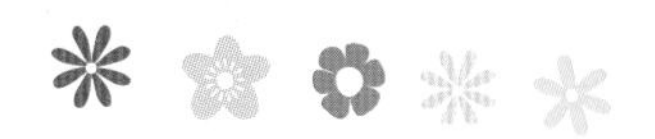

'My best friend has recently started hanging out with a new girl who has just started at my school. I am feeling like she has abandoned me and no longer wants to be my best friend. How should I handle this?'

During your school years, there will always be girls who move homes and go to other schools. Or you will have new girls arrive in your class. This often changes the dynamics of social groups at school. It can be difficult when you feel that things are different and no longer like they were. Take time to meet the new girl, rather than focus on your best friend hanging out with her. You might just find you have a terrific opportunity to make a new friend.

A clash of personalities

Sometimes, you will find that you are in a class at school or even in a family or sports team with someone who just annoys you. This can sometimes be caused by a clash of personality. For example, you may be a **QUIET** and **SHY** person and like to have a little peace and quiet around you. However there might be a friend or family member around you who likes to be the centre of attention and is often **LOUD** and very **VOCAL!**

You might feel **FRUSTRATED** or even a little angry at how this person behaves. It might really, really annoy you!

But here's the thing...

EVERYONE has been created by God as unique and different. Some are loud, energetic and always talking or giving their opinions, while others are less talkative and like to listen to what others are saying – not voicing their opinions too often. That doesn't mean that they are terrible people. It just means they are different to **YOU!**

Learning tolerance

As friends, we all need to learn tolerance, because sometimes we will be friends with others who do frustrate us by the way they behave. It can easily get us down. We all need to learn to tolerate others and their personalities. You can't always control who you will spend time with – whether that be friends on your netball or basketball team, or relatives at a big family barbeque. Sometimes you need to smile and remember to be interested in what others have to say.

Being tolerant **DOESN'T** mean you have to put up with behaviour that is unacceptable, such as bullying, gossiping or physical threats. This is never okay. But just remember that one day you will be out in the big wide world working in a job, and you can't control the different personalities you will work with. So learning to get along with others and accept that we are all different is a part of growing up.

You cannot control others' behaviours, but you can always control **YOUR OWN!**

Gossip

'Watch the way you talk. Let nothing foul or dirty come out of your mouth. Say only what helps, each word a gift.'

Ephesians 4:29 (MSG)

Gossip is the term used to describe talking about a friend or someone else behind her back. If it feels strange to be talking about a person when she is not around, it may be **GOSSIP**.

Hurtful gossiping and spreading **RUMOURS** (lies/untruths) can be one of the most difficult parts of being a girl.

Gossiping is pretty easy to define – it is anything said that you wouldn't be perfectly happy to say **IN FRONT** of the person you're talking about.

Gossip can be one of the most **UPSETTING** things a girl can experience within her social groups. It can be a bit like lighting a match in the middle of a forest. At first, only a few small twigs are lit and a small flame grows, then that flame catches onto another branch and before you know it, the whole forest is on fire and many precious trees and animals can be destroyed.

When I was a young girl, there was a game in which we would all sit in a circle. Someone would start off by saying a sentence quietly into the ear of another person next to them. That person would then whisper what she heard into the ear of the person next to her. And on it would go – right around the circle. Finally, the message would reach the last person in the circle. She would say out loud what she heard and we'd often laugh at how **DIFFERENT** it was to the original sentence.

What happened to the original message? It got lost along the way, bit by bit. Little parts would be misheard and someone would guess a word to fit in.

Life's a bit like that too. Little bits of information get lost as a story is retold over and over.

As people pass on information about another person, they can often add their own slant on a story or over-exaggerate parts that sound better. By the time the hurtful gossip gets around, it can be very **FAR REMOVED** from the actual truth. That's when damage can be done to the subject of the gossip.

There is a really simple guideline for working out if something is gossip or not. Ask yourself the following question before continuing to pass on information:

> **'Will this information/these words build the other person up (make them feel great about themselves), or damage that person's self-image and make them feel bad?'**

It's pretty simple, really. You should know in your heart whether the information is helpful or not.

'No matter how much you want to say something negative about someone else – **DON'T!** Things can spread way too fast if you say something to the wrong person, so don't.

'If you hear something being said about a friend, ask the person saying it to stop!'

Tiana, aged 12

'Gossiping is something wrong, something bad. If you spread secrets, the person who it's about may have a permanent scar. They will never be able to totally forget about it. This person can't talk to her friends any more because they have hurt her too many times.

Are you one of the friends? Do you treat your friends this way? Well if you are, you need to know that it's not the right way to treat your friends.

Soon it won't be a problem though, because you won't have any friends left.

Taylor, aged 12

'Gossip is when you hear something you like about someone you don't.'

Earl Wilson

Is it gossip?

If you are not sure if what you are about to say is GOSSIP, read through the checklist below.

Would you say it if the person was standing right next to you?

If the answer is NO, then it is probably gossip.

Are you only repeating this information to make YOURSELF feel better?

Would this information build the person up or tear them down?

If it won't build the person up, it's best left **UNSAID.**

Does it feel like something you should repeat?

If it doesn't feel okay, it probably ISN'T.

Is it something that will affect how others will view the person you are talking about?

Will other people benefit from hearing this information?

If not, it may just be GOSSIP.

'Don't be bluffed into silence by the threats of bullies. There's nothing they can do to your soul, your core being.'

Matthew 10:28 (MSG)

'So live that you wouldn't be ashamed to sell the family parrot to the town gossip.'

Will Rogers

'Gossip is the art of saying nothing in a way that leaves practically nothing unsaid.'

Walter Winchell

GOS

'The only time people dislike gossip is when you gossip about them.'

Will Rogers

'For the Scriptures say, "If you want to enjoy life and see many happy days keep your tongue from speaking evil and your lips from telling lies."'

1 Peter 3:10 (NLT)

'Whoever gossips to you will gossip about you.'

Spanish Proverb

'Gossip needs no carriage.'

Russian proverb

'When of a gossiping circle it was asked, "What are they doing?" The answer was, "swapping lies".'

Richard Brinsley Sheridan

'Listening to gossip is like eating cheap candy; do you want junk like that in your belly?'

Proverbs 26:22 (MSG)

'The tongue can bring death or life; those who love to talk will reap the consequences.'

Proverbs 18:21 (NLT)

SIP

'Don't talk out of both sides of your mouth; avoid careless banter, white lies, and gossip.'

Proverbs 4:24 (MSG)

'A gadabout gossip can't be trusted with a secret, but someone of integrity won't violate a confidence.'

Proverbs 11:13 (MSG)

'The loose tongue of the godless spreads destruction; the common sense of the godly preserves them.'

Proverbs 11:9 (MSG)

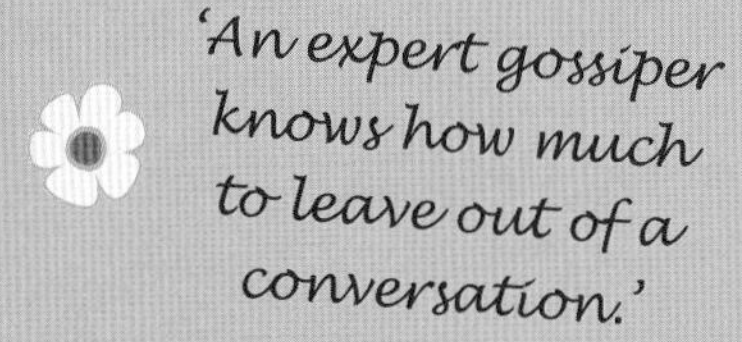

'An expert gossiper knows how much to leave out of a conversation.'

Author unknown

'Conversation is an exercise of the mind; gossip is merely an exercise of the tongue.'

Author unknown

'Kind words are like honey – sweet to the soul and healthy for the body.'

Proverbs 16:24 (NLT)

'Gossip is only the lack of a worthy memory.'

Elbert Hubbard

It's okay to be YOU!

Real friends don't expect YOU to change

When I was growing up, I used to worry about getting the giggles at inappropriate times, such as in the middle of class. And I was super embarrassed about needing glasses and struggling to see the blackboard in class.

The thing to remember is, others *may* actually **LOVE** the things that you regard as **WEIRD** characteristics.

'You can always tell a real friend: when you've made a fool of yourself he doesn't feel you've done a permanent job.'

Laurence J. Peter

Just think about it – if you are the **TALKATIVE** friend in a group, that might actually be the role you are **MEANT** to play. Having you as a friend probably gets conversations going, and gives quieter girls time to think about what they might say.

Maybe **YOU** are the one who finds humour in situations that others find difficult. That can help everyone lighten up.

Of course, don't assume everything you do is fantastic. You're going to have to change some behaviours or at least consider others.

For example, think first before sharing that thought you have. It might save you a lot of heartache later.

The real you – the amazing, gorgeous real you – doesn't need to change!

Never ever **EVER** apologise for being **YOU**!

Dealing with shyness

Many girls are **SHY**. It will feel like your heart is nearly leaping out of your chest at the very thought of being put in a new situation or being confronted with having to make new friends. Being shy is nothing to be embarrassed or worried about. Many girls are shy and get through life just fine.

But if you struggle with feeling shy, on the following pages are a **FEW TIPS** to help you make some friends.

Expect others to like you

When you feel shy, you can also feel like people might not want to talk to you or may not like you. Forget about feeling like that! When you meet new people, go into it with the attitude that they **WILL** like you!

1 Think of five questions you could ask a new person you meet

This gives you some ideas before you are actually faced with a situation in which you may have to talk. So think up some 'ready' questions first.

Here are a few ideas to help you:

* Where do you live?
* How many people make up your family?
* Who is your favourite singer or band?
* What school do you go to or have you been to in the past?
* What are your favourite hobbies/sports?

2 Practise in front of the mirror

If you are **REALLY** shy, you might want to practise asking some of these questions in front of the mirror and watch what your face is doing when you talk.

For example, make sure you are smiling when you ask these questions. Your smiling face will actually help you to relax and will also be a welcoming gesture to the person you are talking to.

Remember, a **SMILE** instantly puts people at ease.

You could also practise talking with a family member at home (brother, sister, mum or dad). Ask them to give you some feedback on how you did.

3 Relax

Take the time to relax before you go into a new situation.

Take 5-10 very deep breaths, put yourself in a positive frame of mind and **SMILE**. A smile is an instant way to relax.

4 Pray

Ask God to bring a **SPECIAL** friend into your life - perhaps one that you haven't met yet!

For girls who are shy!

Don't be at all worried
If you are especially shy.
It just means that you need more practice
At getting out there and saying 'Hi'.

Being shy may just mean
You like to sit and observe,
And listen to others' conversations
It is just a learning curve.

Not every one of us
Loves to be the centre of attention.
Some girls simply have other qualities,
Too many here to mention.

Sometimes it will take some time
For people to know the real you.
And then you may just be surprised
That others may be nervous too.

And if you see another
Sitting on their own,
It may be someone just like you
Who makes them less alone.

For shyness is a quality
Just like confidence and grace.
It may be what makes you special,
Unique in any case!

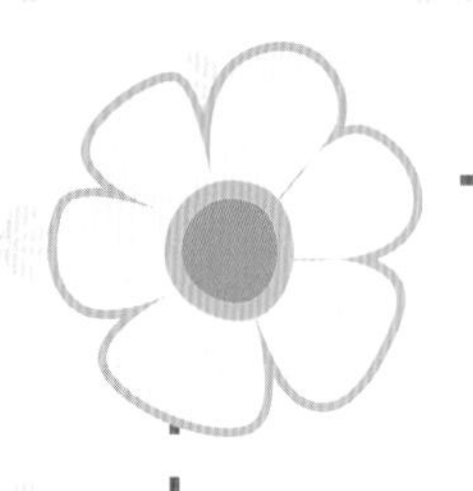

Opposites can attract

JESSICA has a very strong and talkative personality. Whenever she is with a group of friends, she always seems to be the life of the party. She always has an opinion about everything, whether that be who is the greatest, most popular band at the moment, or what game the girls should be playing at breaktime.

PHOEBE is Jessica's very best friend. They have been inseparable since nursery. They have always spent time at each other's homes and have celebrated every birthday together so far. Phoebe, however, is a quiet girl, and incredibly thoughtful. When you see the girls together, it can be difficult to see how they can be such good friends. You might imagine that Jessica would do **ALL** of the talking and Phoebe would spend a lot of time simply listening to Jess.

Even though the two friends are quite **DIFFERENT**, they have both learnt a lot from each other. Phoebe is very thoughtful and quiet, so she will often write Jessica lovely notes and cards that **ENCOURAGE** her. This teaches Jess to think more about others and how lovely it is to be an encourager.

Phoebe has also learnt some communication skills through observing conversations with her friend Jess. She has learnt how to begin a conversation about a topic of her choice. She has also learnt self-confidence by doing other things she wouldn't normally attempt with her friend such as writing and performing a play together in front of their families at Christmas.

Think about some of your friends that have a different personality to you.

Think of **THREE** friends you have who are different in some way to you. List the qualities or talents they have that are **DIFFERENT** to yours and how that might help you develop as a person.

Example:

Cathy

Encouraging, great at craft, loves to sing.

How I can learn from her?

I can learn to encourage my friends more. I can write songs and ask her to record them for me.

Friend #1 ______________________

Qualities/talents they have that are different from mine:

____

How I can learn from them?

____

____

Friend #2

Qualities/talents they have that are different from mine:

How I can learn from them?

Friend #3

Qualities/talents they have that are different from mine:

How I can learn from them?

Be a FRIEND to yourself

Sometimes, you might find it difficult to relate to others. Perhaps you are having a bad day or a terrible week.

In order to be a good friend to others, it is really important to actually be a good friend to **YOURSELF!**

I bet this sounds pretty strange, hey?

Let me explain.

Firstly, we actually teach others how to treat **US.** So if we are always putting ourselves down in front of our friends, using phrases such as **'I'M SO UGLY'** or **'I'M HOPELESS AT WRITING'**, **'I HATE MY CURLY HAIR'**, **'I'M SO CLUMSY'** or **'I'M TERRIBLE AT SPORT'** then, well... You get the picture!

You are teaching your friends and peers that it's okay to talk to you that way and treat you like that, because that is how you treat yourself.

Can you imagine yourself saying to a friend, 'Your hair looks terrible today' or '**NOBODY LIKES YOU**'?

I bet you are shocked at such a thought.

You see, you wouldn't say these things to a friend, but so often these are the very words we say to ourselves. Perhaps we don't do so out loud, but maybe just in our own minds.

Treat yourself with love and respect.

Always speak kindly and positively to yourself.

Treat yourself as you would like others to treat you.

There is a great verse in the Bible that says:

'Do to others as you would like them to do to you.'
Luke 6:31 (NLT)

So make sure that you treat yourself as you would like to be treated by others, too.

Friends are a blessing.
You may find them in the most unlikely of places.

Real friends listen to you and allow you to
share your deepest thoughts and dreams.

Imagine a world without friends
- it would be plain dreary.

Encouraging one another
is what friends do for each other.

Now and then you may experience changes
in your friendships - but all friends come into
your life for a reason.

Don't underestimate the importance of
friends that are loyal and supportive
- they are sometimes difficult to find.

Spend time nurturing your friendships
- that way they will grow strong and sturdy.

FUN THINGS
TO DO
WITH YOUR
FRIENDS

'I love going to sleepovers with friends – staying up late, watching movies, talking and giggling.'

Jess, aged 10

'I love playing tennis with my friends. It's great to have a sport in common that you really enjoy.'

Renee, aged 11

Wha
you
thing
wi

'I love going bowling with my friends or seeing a movie together. It's fun to find things in common and occasionally try something new.'

Carlie, aged 10

'I love sitting painting our nails, telling each other our secrets.'

Chloe, aged 10

'I enjoy playing in the playground at school with my friends.'

Bek, aged 8

'My friends and I write funny scripts together and make mini-movies... they are hilarious!'

Em, aged 11

'I enjoy walking, talking with my friends about strange and funny things.'

Bella, aged 9

re
AVOURITE
o do
our
riends?

'I love to have fun by joking around and taking photos and videos with my friends. Basically, making fun memories together.'

Kellie, aged 10

My friend and
ve to play outside
in the garden.
e imagine we are
dventurers in the
wilderness.'

Katie, aged 10

'My friend Indi and I play on the red monkey bars every day. It is a long way down. We can do front flips and back flips, and "back flip front flip" we made up ourselves. It is fun!'

Erin Whitelaw, aged 7

Chocolate balls recipe

Make some yummy treats with your friends.

Equipment

- ✔ 2 Mixing bowls
- ✔ Wooden spoon
- ✔ Rolling pin
- ✔ Kitchen scales
- ✔ Plastic food bag
- ✔ Baking tray or plastic tray (to go in fridge)

Ingredients

- ✔ 350g packet of 'Marie' biscuits
- ✔ 100g of desiccated coconut
- ✔ 1 x 395g can of sweetened condensed milk
- ✔ 50g of cocoa
- ✔ Extra coconut for rolling balls in

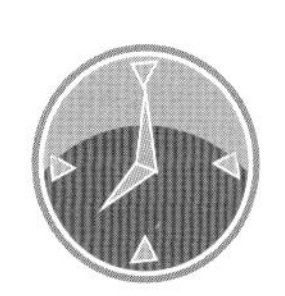

Time: 30 minutes to 1 hour.

Method

1. Place the packet of biscuits into the plastic food bag.
2. Using the rolling pin, gently crush all of the biscuits until they are **VERY FINE** crumbs.
3. Put the biscuit crumbs, the sweetened condensed milk, cocoa and coconut into the mixing bowl.
4. Mix well until they are completely mixed together. The mixture will be very **STICKY!**
5. Put the extra coconut in a separate bowl.
6. Wash your hands well, but don't dry them because it's much easier to roll the chocolate balls with **WET HANDS.**
7. Take a small scoop of mixture with your hands and roll it into a ball. Then roll the ball into the bowl of coconut and set the completed ball onto the tray. You **WON'T** be cooking these, so you can use a plastic tray of you like.
8. Continue the process until all the balls have been completed. (You will probably have to wash your hands a lot of times as the mixture gets very **STICKY** and **GOOEY.**)
9. Place the tray of chocolate balls into the fridge for an hour. Once they are cold they will harden and then they are ready to eat.

ENJOY! ☺

Friendship affirmation journals

You will need:

- ✔ A small notebook or exercise book
- ✔ Scrapbooking paper or wrapping paper
- ✔ Stickers and embellishments
- ✔ Ribbons
- ✔ Gel pens

Method

1. Trace and cut out scrapbooking or wrapping paper of your choice to fit as a cover for your journal.
2. Glue cover paper onto your journal.
3. You are now free to decorate the outside of your journal with stickers, your name and pictures.
4. Glue in quotes, stickers and embellishments in the inside pages of your journal.
5. Make journals with each of your friends.
6. Now you can pass your journal around to each other and take turns to write some encouraging notes and messages to each other.

JUST 4 FUN

Painting a friendship canvas

You will need:

- ✔ Mini canvases (to paint on) available from discount stores and craft supply stores
- ✔ Assortment of paints
- ✔ Paintbrushes and palette
- ✔ Embellishments and craft glue (to adding some sparkles)
- ✔ Ribbon to attach to canvas

Method

1. Paint a bold colour (base coat) over the canvas first.
2. Sketch a design on the canvas once it is dry. Or you could just paint your picture straight onto the background if you are confident.
3. You can then decorate each other's canvases together or paint one each for yourselves.
4. Once the paint has dried completely, use craft glue to add some sparkles or embellishments if you like.
5. Pin or glue ribbon to the top (or across the back from side to side) of the canvas (see picture above) so that you can hang it on your bedroom wall. ☺

COOL IDEA: You could even paste on your favourite friendship quote once you've finished painting your canvas, then paint one layer of **CRAFT GLUE** over the top to seal it.

JUST 4 FUN

Making a friendship board

This makes a great decoration to hang in your bedroom and also serves as a wonderful reminder of the BLESSINGS of your friends. ☺

You will need:

- ✔ Pin board or large photo frame (available from most department or stationery stores)
- ✔ Assorted craft supplies: scrapbook paper, scissors, glue stick, ribbons and embellishments
- ✔ Favourite friendship quotes
- ✔ Photographs of you and your friends

What to do next:

If you are using a **LARGE PHOTO FRAME**, carefully take the back of the photo frame off (ask your mum or dad for help with this!) and re-cover the inside board using your favourite scrapbook paper. You can then paste photographs and friendship quotes onto the paper. Put the board back into the photo frame and join together again, ready to display on your bookshelf or hang on your bedroom wall.

A **LARGE PIN BOARD** is also a great idea to use for a friendship board. You can choose to cover the entire board with some bright fabric first, and then pin a variety of photographs, cards, memories and quotes on to it. The other great thing about using a pin board is that it is easy to change and update as often as you like!

Helping a friend

When a friend is sick:

- Pray for her.
- Call her on the phone to wish her well and send good wishes that she will recover soon.
- Make and then post a 'Get Well' card.
- Make a card and ask all of your classmates or close friends to write positive messages.

'If your gift is to encourage others, be encouraging. If it is giving, give generously. If God has given you leadership ability, take the responsibility seriously. And if you have a gift for showing kindness to others, do it gladly. Don't just pretend to love others. Really love them. Hate what is wrong. Hold tightly to what is good.'

Romans 12:8-9 (NLT)

When a friend is in hospital:

If a friend is in hospital for any length of time, you can ask your teacher if you can organise classmates to each write a **LETTER** to the friend in hospital. Ask your parent or teacher to find out the name, address and ward number of the hospital. Ask that one letter be posted every day your friend is there.

Make up a **CARE PACKAGE** for your friend. Little things can help pass the time for a person in hospital. You could purchase a lovely gift box from a discount store and include things for your friend, such as:

- games
- puzzles
- photographs of friends
- books
- hand cream
- hair ties
- hairbrush
- positive affirmations and notes

When a friend loses a pet or someone dearly loved:

- Send a special card with your best wishes.
- See if you are able to get hold of a photo of her loved one and put it in a frame.
- Spend some extra time with your friend and give her a chance to just talk about her pet and show you pictures.
- Pick some flowers from your garden and give them to her.
- Pray for peace.

When a friend is away from school for a long time:

- Write a letter or a card and tell her you are missing her. Post it to your friend's home.
- Make a card and ask all of her school friends to sign it with a special message.
- Call her on the phone and ask her how she is doing. Remind her that she is missed at school.
- Start a prayer chain or a prayer group where all her friends take turns praying for her.

CONFLICT RESOLUTION

Bullying

Bullying is unfortunately something that many young girls experience at some stage in their lives. It can take on many forms, from just one person bullying you to an entire group. It can be verbal, meaning it's all hurtful words, or bullying can be physical, where a person hurts you.

Sometimes, someone might bully you by writing nasty and hurtful notes. Or the bully might talk behind your back to others (gossip). Or the person might be really **BOLD** and just speak in a nasty way to your face, often more than once. Sometimes, they might **DELIBERATELY** leave you out of a conversation or social group.

'Friendship is like a mirror. Once it's broken it is very hard to put back together.'

Aisha Dalal

When someone picks on you **CONSISTENTLY** (often, or all the time), that is called bullying, and it is **NOT OKAY**. Every girl deserves the right to feel safe and happy.

A bullying story...

In Year 5 at school, I was bullied by a girl who I thought was my best friend. I was so upset because all of my other friends went off with her and left me alone. I had no one!

One day, we went to music and I went up to ask a question of the teacher. This girl just put her leg out and I fell off the stairs. I hurt my hand and had to tell the teacher. However, she wasn't terribly helpful. She just said something like 'That's life'.

Celeste, aged 12

Examples of bullying

 Physically hitting, punching or shoving another person intentionally.

 Name calling.

 Deliberately provoking someone, making fun of them.

 Encouraging someone to do something they do not want to do.

 Excluding someone from a group's activities.

 Gossiping.

 Writing hurtful notes, letters or text messages.

Tips for dealing with BULLYING

It is not a nice feeling at all to be bullied.

If you are being bullied, you might feel:

These are quite **NORMAL FEELINGS** when people are hurting you. One of the things that a bully tries to do is take away your power. By leaving you out of a friendship group or saying nasty things to you, a bully wants you to feel **SAD** and SMALL.

If you are feeling this way, it is important that you ask for **HELP**. This is a big step and not always easy to do.

You might even feel EMBARRASSED that you are the target of a bully. So it is important for you to know that it is not your fault. And it has to **STOP**.

'So in everything, do to others what you would have them do to you.'
Matthew 7:12a (NIV)

What you can do if you are being BULLIED

Ask the person who is bullying you to STOP it. This may be enough for the other person to realise that what they have been doing is not kind and has made you feel very sad.

If the person does not stop the behaviour after you have asked, it is time to ask an adult for some HELP.

It is important that you talk to a trusted adult about how you are feeling. This might be your teacher, mum or dad, Sunday school teacher or youth group leader.

They will be able to give you some ideas about how you can deal with the person who is hurting you.

They might suggest that you write a **LETTER** to the person, explaining how his or her behaviour is affecting you and asking them to **STOP IT!**

Your teacher might suggest **MEETING** with you and the other person together so you have the chance to share how you are feeling and how their behaviour affects you.

Or perhaps the teacher might talk to the person who is upsetting you and help that person to see that what he or she is doing is not kind behaviour.

If the behaviour continues, **KEEP TALKING** with a trusted adult until it stops.

No one ever deserves to be bullied!

Dealing with CONFLICT with friends

It can be so difficult when you have a misunderstanding or fall out with friends. I would love to tell you that it will hardly ever happen but sadly, when we are dealing with people who have different personalities, misunderstandings and conflicts will happen sometimes.

Now, you can try and avoid conflict as much as you like, but it will only keep you tied up in knots. It is best to try and COMMUNICATE your feelings with the person who has hurt you, whilst at the same time trying to be mindful of their feelings.

Identify your own FEELINGS

How are you feeling right now about the problem you are having with your friend?

Circle the following pictures that best describe how you are feeling at the moment:

TIPS for talking through problems with your friends

- Make sure you are **CALM** before you talk to your friend about how you are feeling. Trying to explain how you are feeling when you are upset will only make things difficult, so make sure you are calm.
- Choose the **RIGHT TIME** to talk. Avoid a time such as straight before class starts or at the end of lunchtime. When it is a good time, mention to your friend first that you would like to have a chat. Give them some time to prepare for your talk.
- Make sure you talk **FACE TO FACE**. Emailing, texting or talking over the phone is difficult and may lead to a misunderstanding, perhaps making things even more awkward.
- Talk to an **ADULT** (parent or teacher) about your problem. They might be able to give you some helpful advice about the best way to approach the issue.
- Think about your **BODY LANGUAGE** and **FACIAL EXPRESSIONS** before you begin your conversation with your friend. Even if you are feeling very hurt or angry,

have a **PLEASANT** look on your face. It will help the other person not to feel that you are attacking her.

* When you talk to your friend about how you are feeling, try using 'I' statements. That releases any blame towards the person you are talking to. Here are some ideas to get the conversation going:

'I've been feeling really lonely when you have been off playing with the other girls. I know you probably don't realise it, but I feel sad and would love to be included.'

'When you say things to me but then say you are only joking, I find that difficult. Because in my head I know you are joking but in my heart I still feel hurt.'

'Now that Sarah has come to our school, I sometimes feel like our friendship has changed. I really like to hang out with you and really appreciate our friendship. I sometimes feel lonely. Do you think you could make sure I get included?'

Friendship

'Since you get more joy out of giving joy to others, you should put a good deal of thought into the happiness that you are able to give.'

Eleanor Roosevelt

'A friend is one who knows you and loves you just the same.'

Elbert Hubbard

'True friendship comes when the silence between two people is comfortable.'

David Tyson Gentry

'Fate chooses your relations, you choose your friends.'

Jacques Delille

'Don't befriend angry people or associate with hot-tempered people, or you will learn to be like them and endanger your soul.'

Proverbs 22:24–25 (NLT)

'Perfume and incense bring joy to the heart, and the pleasantness of a friend springs from their heartfelt advice.'

Proverbs 27:9 (NIV)

'A sweet friendship refreshes the soul.'

Proverbs 27:9b (MSG)

'A friend is a person with a sneaky knack of saying good things about you behind your back.'

Marilyn Jansen

'Hold a true friend with both your hands.'

Nigerian proverb

'When you listen to your friends, when you encourage them, when you do things their way (at least sometimes), you're really telling them, "I'm glad you're my friend".'

Bob & Emilie Barnes

uotes

'To the world you may be just one person, but to one person you may be the world.'

Unknown

'There are "friends" who destroy each other, but a real friend sticks closer than a brother.'

Proverbs 18:24 (NLT)

'Make sure that nobody pays back wrong for wrong, but always strive to do what is good for each other and for everyone else.'

1 Thessalonians 5:15 (NIV)

In conclusion...

Well here you are at the end of the book!

Thank you for reading **GIRL WISE**. I hope that you have learnt some valuable things about being a **GOOD FRIEND** to others and making and valuing your friends.

As I write this conclusion, I have just returned from a special dinner with two of my best girlfriends that have been my friends since high school. We have now been friends for 25 years! (I know – that's ages, right?)

Well, my hope and prayer for you – special girl – is that the friendships you make will impact your life in some **WONDERFUL WAY**. Some friends will be in your life for a reason, and some for just a season. And some will become lifelong friends, which are all the more **SPECIAL**.

Take care

Love

Sharon